About the Author

Tara Thorpe, earlier called 'Tiny' by some due to her diminutive stature, grew in height and intellect at Bromsgrove School in Worcestershire, England. Her early interest in all things ancient led her to gain a bachelor's degree in Classics at The University of Birmingham and a master's degree in Ancient History at King's College London. Fearing the lack of exposure to such subjects within the normal everyday activities of modern youngsters and, indeed, within the current school curriculum, Tara wished to spur interest in Greek Mythology and penned *Mini Myths* as a taster for the magical wonders that await those who dare to delve further.

BUMBLEBEE PAPERBACK EDITION

Copyright © Tara Thorpe 2021
Illustrations by Marta Maszkiewicz

A CIP catalogue record for this title is
available from the British Library.

ISBN: 978-1-83934-252-3

Bumblebee Books is an imprint of
Olympia Publishers.

First Published in 2021

Bumblebee Books
Tallis House
2 Tallis Street
London
EC4Y 0AB

Printed in Great Britain

www.olympiapublishers.com

Tara Thorpe
Illustrations by Marta Maszkiewicz

Mini Myths 1-4
A Collection of Ancient Greek
Myths for Children

Bumblebee Books
London

THE MYTH OF THE JUDGEMENT OF PARIS

Zeus (zee-use) was King of the Gods, Sky Father, Cloud Gatherer. Thunder and lightning were his to command and his power was awesomely great.

Zeus fell in love with the sea-nymph, **Thetis** (thee-tis). A prophecy, however, warned that if **Thetis** had a son, that son could be greater than his father. **Zeus** would not let this happen. So, **Zeus** makes **Peleus** (pee-lee-us), a Greek king, fall in love with **Thetis** and they end up marrying. The marriage of **Thetis** to a mortal, **Peleus**, means their child would also be a mortal, so the child would not be a threat to **Zeus**.

All the gods were invited to the magnificent wedding of **Peleus** and **Thetis**, apart from **Eris** (air-is), the goddess of discord. This was an obvious exclusion because **Eris** was known to cause a lot of disruption and mischief. Despite this, **Eris** showed up anyway and rolls into the crowd of wedding guests an apple, 'the apple of discord'.

Three goddesses – **Hera** (hair-a), Queen of the gods; **Athena** (a-thee-na), goddess of war and wisdom and **Aphrodite** (afro-die-tea), goddess of love and beauty – pick up the apple and see the words 'for the fairest' written on the apple. Each goddess wants the prize for herself.

Zeus commands **Hermes** (her-meez), messenger of the gods, to lead the goddesses to **Paris** (pa-riss), Prince of Troy, who will make the decision. Troy was an ancient city located on the coast of Asia Minor, which is modern day Turkey. Each goddess offers **Paris** gifts for his favour. **Paris** chooses **Aphrodite**. **Paris** was swayed by his promised marriage to **Helen**, the most beautiful mortal, which **Aphrodite** (afro-die-tea), offered to him. **Hera** (hair-a) had offered **Paris** the gift to be king of all men and **Athena** had offered him victory in war – but these would not satisfy **Paris** as much as marrying **Helen** with her stunning beauty.

  Paris judgement set in motion the events which would eventually lead to the famous Trojan War. This famous war is one of the most important events in Greek mythology.

THE MYTH OF ACHILLES' HEEL

Achilles (a-kill-eez) was the greatest of all Greek warriors and was the hero of the Trojan War.

He was the son of the Greek king **Peleus** (pee-lee-us) and the sea-nymph **Thetis** (thee-tis). **Achilles** was superhumanly strong, deeply loyal, brave and he was an extraordinary warrior.

When **Achilles** was born, his mother, **Thetis**, was told that he would die young, heroically in battle. To be a great warrior was the fate of **Achilles**. Unlike **Thetis**, who was a sea-nymph, **Achilles** was a mortal like his father. So, **Thetis** tried to make him immortal like the gods by dipping him into the river Styx – a magical river that formed the boundary between Earth and the Underworld. Its magical waters were said to give the gift of immortality to anything or anyone that was dipped into it. As **Thetis** held **Achilles** by his heel, it was not touched by the river, so this part of his body was left vulnerable and weak.

In the Trojan War, **Achilles** met his fate and died from a wound to his heel, which was the result of an arrow shot by **Paris** (pa-riss), prince of Troy.

When you hear the term 'Achilles heel' this is where it comes from. It has come to mean a point of weakness in someone or something, despite overall strength.

The Myth of the Trojan Horse

The tale of the ancient city of Troy and the war that was fought there, has been told for some three-thousand years. Troy was located in what is now Turkey and looked across the sea westwards to Greece.

The war started because King **Priam** (pr-eye- am) of Troy's son, **Paris** (pa-riss), fell in love with **Helen** (hell-en), who was said to be the most beautiful mortal in the world. **Helen** was the wife of King **Menelaus** (men-uh-lay-us) of Sparta, in Greece. **Paris** abducted **Helen** and took her back to Troy. Furious, **Menelaus** demanded her return, but the Trojans refused and so **Menelaus** persuaded his brother, **Agamemnon**, to lead an army against Troy.

In the tenth year of the war, one of the Greek generals and King of Ithaca, **Odysseus**, thought up a brilliant idea. With the help of **Athena** (a-thee-na), the goddess of war and wisdom, the Greeks built a huge wooden horse and left it outside the gates of Troy, as a gift to the gods. The horse was built by **Epeius** (ep-eye-us), a master carpenter. It was gigantic and importantly, it was hollow.

The Greeks pretended to give up and sail off. But actually, they sail to the nearby island of Tenedos whilst several warriors secretly hide inside the great hollow horse.

Despite warnings, the Trojans fall for the trick and bring the wooden horse into the city. During the night, as the Trojans were sleeping, the warriors who had been hiding inside the horse rush out and opened the city gates. The waiting Greek army enter and they sack the famous city.

The magnificent city of Troy burns, and falls.

As the saying goes, 'beware of Greeks bearing gifts!'

THE MYTH OF ODYSSEUS AND THE CYCLOPS

Odysseus (oh-diss-ee-yus) was the legendary king of the Greek island Ithaca. He is famous for his intellect and his clever tricks.

After the Trojan War, he set sail home for Ithaca with his men. But his journey home did not go smoothly. After many obstacles and adventures, **Odysseus** and his men come to an island inhabited by the Cyclopes. The Cyclopes were one-eyed giants.

Odysseus and his men find a cave on the island and help themselves to food and drink before falling asleep. The cave, however, was home to a Cyclops called **Polyphemus** (polly-fee-muss), son of **Poseidon** (po-sigh-don), god of the sea. That evening **Polyphemus** returns home, blocking the entrance of the cave with a huge stone.

Polyphemus finds the men inside his cave and is hospitable to the men at first, but he soon turns unfriendly. **Polyphemus** decides to make a meal out of some of **Odysseus**'s men and eats them up. **Polyphemus** imprisons **Odysseus** and the rest of his men in the cave for future meals. Scared for his and his men's lives, **Odysseus** wants to kill **Polyphemus** right then, but he realises that he wouldn't be able to get out. Only **Polyphemus** is strong enough to move the stone blocking the entrance.

Desperate to escape, **Odysseus** comes up with a plan. **Odysseus** was famous for his clever plans. **Odysseus** offers **Polyphemus** some very strong wine given to him earlier on his journey. **Polyphemus** asks **Odysseus** his name in a very slurred way (the effects of the strong wine were working). **Odysseus** cleverly replies that his name is 'Nobody'. After this, **Polyphemus** falls into a drunken sleep. Meanwhile, **Odysseus** and his men drive a wooden stake into **Polyphemus**'s eye. **Polyphemus** awoke in agony, screaming. Shouting for help to the other Cyclopes on the island, **Polyphemus** says that 'Nobody' has hurt him. This was part of **Odysseus**'s plan so that no one would come to his rescue. Nobody did.

The following morning, when the now blind Cyclops lets his sheep out to graze, **Odysseus**'s clever planning continues. He and his remaining, non-eaten, men tie themselves to the bellies of **Polyphemus**'s sheep, before they're let out of the cave to graze. Whilst **Polyphemus** strokes the back of his sheep, he has no idea that **Odysseus** and his men are tied beneath. They escape successfully.

As he sails off, **Odysseus** boastfully shouts back to **Polyphemus**, revealing his true identity. This was a silly mistake because now **Polyphemus** knows exactly who to avenge. **Polyphemus** throws a huge boulder, narrowly missing **Odysseus**'s ship, and prays that his father, **Poseidon**, takes revenge on **Odysseus**.

As god of the sea, **Poseidon** causes great difficulty on **Odysseus**'s journey home to Ithaca. It eventually takes him ten years to return home.